Beware th

by Alan Da

Illustrated by Jeff Anderson
Series Editors: Steve Barlow and Steve Skidmore

Published by Ginn and Company
Halley Court, Jordan Hill, Oxford OX2 8EJ
A division of Reed Educational and Professional Publishing Ltd
Telephone number for ordering **Impact**: 01865 888084

OXFORD   MELBOURNE   AUCKLAND   JOHANNESBURG
BLANTYRE GABORONE   IBADAN   PORTSMOUTH (NH)
USA   CHICAGO

First published 1999

2003 2002 2001 2000 99

10 9 8 7 6 5 4 3 2 1

ISBN 0 435 21234 6

Illustrations
Jeff Anderson / Pennant Illustration

Cover artwork
Kevin Jenkins

Designed by Shireen Nathoo Design

Printed and bound in Great Britain by Thomson Litho Ltd

Contents

The Characters

JON

Jon is 14. He can
be shy. He is good
friends with Sam.

SAM

Sam is 14. He is full of
self-confidence. He likes to
stir up trouble for others, but
is a good friend to Jon.

ROBBO

Robbo is 14. He is the school
bully and likes to act tough.

MR FOWLER

Mr Fowler is the
school caretaker.

Scene One

The school playground. Robbo walks over to Sam and Jon, who are standing together.

ROBBO: I've been looking for you.

JON: I don't want any trouble, Robbo.

ROBBO: You've got something I need. Remember?

SAM: What's that? Brains?

ROBBO: *(Crossly)* Very funny. *(He takes Jon's bag and looks inside.)*

JON: You won't find any in there.

ROBBO: *(Holds up Jon's maths book.)* Just what the teacher ordered. *(He rips out several pages and stuffs them in his pocket.)* Thanks, Jon. I would have done it myself, only you've saved me the bother.

JON: Mrs Stone will know it isn't your handwriting.

ROBBO: Do I look stupid? I'm going to copy it, aren't I?

SAM: *(Muttering)* You're scared she'll find out!

ROBBO: I'm not scared of anybody in this school. I do what I want and I go where I want, right?

SAM: I bet there's one place you won't go. *(He points to the old school building.)* Over there. The old school. Top floor. Where the ghosts are. *(He pretends to be a ghost, pulling his sweatshirt over his head.)* Whoooo!

ROBBO:	Been there ... done it ... got the tee shirt. There's nothing on the top floor but old desks and dust. All that stuff about people hearing noises and seeing lights at the window is... rubbish. Spread about by the caretaker to stop us lot going inside. He's probably sick of picking up cigarette ends. *(A pause.)* I've never seen you two on the top floor.
SAM:	I'm scared of heights.
ROBBO:	*(To Jon)* What's your excuse?
JON:	Leave me out of it.
SAM:	Jon's not afraid. He'd go up there, no sweat. Any time. *(Jon frowns.)* Not by himself, though. You'd have to tag along, Robbo. Unless you're a ... *(Makes 'chicken' noises.)*
ROBBO:	*(Grinning)* If he's in, I'm in.
SAM:	Jon?
JON:	*(A pause)* What if the caretaker catches us?
ROBBO:	Sounds like you're the chicken.
JON:	*(Annoyed)* Okay, I'll go.
SAM:	That's settled, then. You'll need some rules. Rule one. You both stay overnight.
JON:	Come off it, Sam. You've been watching too many cheap horror films.

ROBBO:	Scare the chicken too much and it'll lay an egg.
JON:	I'm no chicken.
SAM:	Rule two. You both get your kit and meet back here in one hour. Shake on it?

(Robbo holds out his hand. Jon looks unsure but shakes it. Robbo leaves, grinning.)

JON:	Thanks a lot, pal.
SAM:	It's only for one night.
JON:	This is worse than the time you set me up on a blind date with your sister.
SAM:	If you go through with this then I swear Robbo will get off your back.

JON:	*(Sounding uncertain)* Yeah?
SAM:	Trust me. If anyone asks, say you're staying round my house tonight.
JON:	It won't be a problem, Sam. My mum's on night shift and my dad will crash out on the sofa when he gets in from work. No one will even know I've gone. *(Jon pauses and bites his lip uncertainly.)* I'd better get my kit.
SAM:	Good luck.

(Jon shrugs, then exits. Mr Fowler, the caretaker, enters. Sam turns and comes face to face with him.)

SAM:	Oh, hello Mr Fowler.
FOWLER:	Haven't you got a home to go to?

SAM: I was kept back by … Mrs Stone … to finish
            some maths.

FOWLER: I don't like kids hanging around after school.
            This old building's dangerous. If anyone gets
            hurt, you won't get the blame. It'll be me.

SAM: Don't worry, I'm going!

(Sam runs off.)

FOWLER: Oi! Who said you could take a shortcut
            through the bushes?

(Mr Fowler shakes his head and follows Sam.)

Scene Two

A room in the old school building. It is night.
Moonlight streams through a window. The room is dusty.
Old desks and chairs are piled high near a blackboard
and teacher's desk.

Robbo enters. Jon runs in after him. They both carry
torches.

JON: *(Out of breath)* I'm sorry I'm a bit late, Robbo.
         I couldn't find my sleeping bag.

(Jon clumsily knocks over a chair, which clatters to the floor.)

ROBBO:	Shh! That's loud enough to wake the dead!
JON:	I can't see a thing.
ROBBO:	This place is cool.
JON:	*(Unimpressed)* It's freezing.
ROBBO:	Sends shivers down your spine, doesn't it? It reminds me of that ship.
JON:	*(Not really listening)* What ship?

ROBBO:	The one Mrs Mills was going on about in History. It was found drifting on the ocean with no one on board, silent as a grave. What happened to the crew is still a mystery.
JON:	There's no mystery about this room, Robbo. The roof leaked and the heaters packed up. It cost too much to fix so they shut it. End of story. The real mystery is what we're doing here.
ROBBO:	Quit moaning. I'm trying to get us in the mood. Where's your sense of adventure?
JON:	*(Pulls out a sleeping bag)* I forgot to pack it.
ROBBO:	How did you get in?
JON:	The same way you did. Through the open window downstairs.
ROBBO:	Did you shut the window?
JON:	Sort of. It jammed half-way.
ROBBO:	Well, you had better hope Fowler the Prowler doesn't see it.
JON:	Who cares? This whole place gives me the creeps. The sooner I can get out of here, the better.
ROBBO:	*(Looking around)* It's no big deal.
JON:	This is my first time up here, remember?

ROBBO: Mine too.

JON: I thought you told Sam you had been up here loads of times.

ROBBO: I say a lot of things. You know how it is.
            (He grins.) I've got my reputation to think of.

(Jon sighs. Robbo shines his torch towards the blackboard. He walks across the room to stand behind the teacher's desk.)

ROBBO: I've always wanted to do this. *(He pretends he is a teacher and uses a 'teacher's voice'.)* Sit down. No talking at the back. I want to see your homework.

JON: You've already got mine, Robbo. Remember?

ROBBO:	*(Back in his normal voice)* Here. *(Robbo reaches into his pocket, and tosses the homework towards Jon.)* You might as well have it back. I didn't get a chance to copy it.
JON:	I don't know why you took it in the first place. Mrs Stone would know it wasn't your work.
ROBBO:	Why – because it's so brilliant?
JON:	I didn't mean that.
ROBBO:	It's easy for you. You're good at maths.
JON:	It still took me ages, Robbo. *(A pause.)* Look, I could go through it with you, if you want.
ROBBO:	That would take all night.
JON:	We've got all night.

(Jon shines his torch on the homework.)

ROBBO:	Here's the bit I don't get. *(Stabs a finger on the paper.)* Decimals. *(A pause.)* I can't see the point.
JON:	It's easy.
ROBBO:	*(Frowning)* There you go again.
JON:	Look, I'll show you on the blackboard.
ROBBO:	You'll need some chalk. Try the desk.

(Jon goes to the teacher's desk and searches for a piece of chalk. He sweeps the torch beam across the blackboard. Suddenly he stops and calls Robbo over.)

JON: *(Sounding scared)* Robbo, what do you think
              made these scratches?

ROBBO: A knife? Or …

JON: Or what?

ROBBO: It sounds crazy, but they look like
              claw marks.

JON: You think an animal took a swipe at the
              blackboard?

ROBBO: It looks that way.

JON: Are you trying to set me up, Robbo?

ROBBO: No!

JON: *(Mockingly)* What's next, tomato sauce dripping from the walls? I'm not going to fall for it, Robbo. The joke's over!

(Jon climbs into his sleeping bag. The zip won't close properly.)

ROBBO: Please yourself. *(Robbo walks to the window. Moonlight is shining through. He looks out, then freezes. Slowly he backs away from the window, and looks nervously at Jon.)* There's something down there in the bushes.

JON:	*(Not looking up)* I'm not listening, Robbo. This zip is getting on my nerves.
ROBBO:	*(Alarmed)* There *is* something in those bushes.
JON:	*(Looks at Robbo)* Let me guess, a black panther with dripping fangs and sharp claws?
ROBBO:	Try *(His voice rising to a half-shout)* ... a wolf! *(His voice cracks)* With red eyes. Like burning coals.
JON:	You've been reading too many fairy stories. *(Mockingly.)* Oh, what big teeth you have, Grandma.
ROBBO:	I'm not joking, Jon. *(He tips Jon out of his sleeping bag.)* Time to get out of here!
JON:	You go ahead, Robbo. If I stay, that means you lose the bet.
ROBBO:	If you stay, you'll lose more than a bet.
JON:	How do you figure that out?

(There is a howl from outside. Jon stares at Robbo.)

ROBBO:	Now do you believe me?
JON:	I'm dreaming, right?
ROBBO:	This isn't a dream. It's your worst nightmare. *(Robbo goes to the door and opens it.)* Come on, we can get out through that jammed window.

JON:　　　　　If we can get out, then *it* can get in.

(There is the sound of smashing glass.)

ROBBO:　　　　Good point! *(He frantically slams the door shut.)* There's no key!

JON:　　　　　Pile up the desks.

(Jon and Robbo block the door with desks and chairs. Suddenly, they freeze. The sound of creaking stairs echoes through the old building.)

ROBBO: We're in big trouble.

(There is a scratching sound at the door).

JON: It's here!

ROBBO: You're the brainy one. What do we do?

JON: Plan A – we wait for it to get in and eat us.

ROBBO: *(Gives a slow handclap)* Great idea.

JON: Plan B – we make a run for it.

ROBBO: Plan B sounds good.

(The door shudders. Jon and Robbo rush to the window and lever it up.)

ROBBO: Now what?

JON: Now it's your turn to have a bright idea.

ROBBO: Okay. Let's jump.

JON: You're crazy!

(Moonlight lights up the area for a moment.)

ROBBO: We can drop onto that flat roof and leg it
           down the fire escape.

JON: You're a genius.

ROBBO: I know. We'll jump together. After three.

(The door behind them opens sending the desks and chairs tumbling. Jon and Robbo climb onto the window ledge. A wolf howls from behind them.)

ROBBO AND JON: *(Together)* THREE!

(As Robbo and Jon jump, the howling fades away.)

Scene Three

Inside the school library the following morning.
Sam enters. He crosses over to Jon and Robbo who are
sitting in front of a computer.

SAM: I've been looking for you two everywhere.
                (To Robbo.) I never thought I'd find *you* in
                the library.

ROBBO: There's a first time for everything.

JON: We need some information.

SAM:	What about?
JON:	Something we saw last night.
SAM:	Don't tell me. There was a headless ghost and a couple of headless chickens running about.
JON:	You wouldn't believe us if we told you. *(Looks at Sam.)* What's happened to you? You look as if you've been dragged through a hedge backwards.
SAM:	I'm not sure. I remember taking a shortcut through the bushes yesterday. I tripped on something and fell. I practically knocked myself out.
JON:	So much for a shortcut. Sounds more like an uppercut. *(Jon clicks the mouse to bring up some information on the screen.)* This is more like it. I've downloaded anything I can find to do with wolves.
SAM:	You saw a wolf? Are you sure it wasn't a fox?
ROBBO:	It was a wolf. It came out of the bushes. We heard it howl, then it heard us.
JON:	Last night was a full moon, right?
SAM:	Yes.

JON:	Then this is what we actually saw. *(He points at the screen and clicks the mouse to print out the information.)*
SAM:	*(Reads the screen)* A werewolf!
JON:	*(Reads the screen)* Werewolf. A person who changes into a wolf during a full moon. The werewolf roams through the night looking for victims to devour.

ROBBO:	*(Takes the printout and reads the text)* A werewolf must become human again before dawn and hide its wolf skin.
JON:	*(Reads the text)* If the werewolf's skin is destroyed, the werewolf is also destroyed.
ROBBO:	That's it! That's what we've got to do. Find the skin and destroy it.
SAM:	You two have got to be joking!
JON:	We're deadly serious.
SAM:	Where exactly was this werewolf, if you saw one?
ROBBO:	By the caretaker's shed, next to the bushes.
SAM:	And you're sure it really was a werewolf?

ROBBO: Listen, if you'd seen its red eyes and heard that howl, you'd be sure! *(He shivers.)*

SAM: But what is a werewolf doing in this country?

JON: *(Reads from the printout)* The legend of the werewolf can be found worldwide.

SAM: A legend is one thing, but to say that werewolves exist is crazy.

JON: We can prove it. When you see the mess it made of the top floor you'll have to believe us.

ROBBO: Come on. We'll show you.

(All three leave the library. Blackout.)

Scene Four

Lights up. Sam, Jon and Robbo are outside the old school.

They are looking up at the top floor of the old building.

A rope bars entry to the building. A bonfire glows nearby.

ROBBO: Someone's got here before us.

SAM: Maybe there's a way in.

(*Sam lifts the rope and starts to duck under it.*
Mr Fowler enters.)

FOWLER: Oi! Where do you think you're going? This
rope is to stop the likes of you lot getting in!

(*Sam rejoins the others.*)

JON: Why has the building been roped off,
Mr Fowler?

FOWLER:	Because of vandals. They've broken inside and helped themselves to school property.
ROBBO:	What sort of stuff?
FOWLER:	Wouldn't *you* like to know?
ROBBO:	I was just asking, that's all.
FOWLER:	Go on, clear off! You've got better things to do than hang around here.

(Mr Fowler picks up some pieces of broken wood, drops them on the bonfire and leaves. Sam, Jon and Robbo move away.)

SAM:	That's that then. We can't get in. Are you sure you two didn't just trash the place?
JON:	Why would we do that?
SAM:	A full moon makes people do funny things.
JON:	There was nothing funny about last night, Sam.
ROBBO:	*(Thoughtfully)* The way I see it, things aren't adding up.
JON:	What do you mean?
ROBBO:	Mr Fowler said that vandals had been in and taken school property. But the building was almost empty.
JON:	He didn't want us hanging about, that's all.
SAM:	He never does. I don't know why Fowler works here. It's obvious he can't stand kids.

ROBBO: Let's take a look over by the bushes, where we
           saw the werewolf.

JON: Good thinking.

ROBBO: *(To Jon)* See, you're not the only one with
           brains.

*(Robbo, Jon and Sam move across to the bushes and look
underneath.)*

SAM: What are we looking for?

ROBBO: Clues.

SAM: Maybe your four-legged friend has left us a
           lead. Or a collar? *(He laughs, but the other two
           do not.)*

JON:	It was a wolf, not a dog.
SAM:	It was a joke.
ROBBO:	Look! A footprint.

(Jon and Sam join Robbo.)

JON:	Right or left?
ROBBO:	Definitely left.
SAM:	So we're after a werewolf with one leg.
ROBBO:	*(To Jon)* Just ignore him.
JON:	What were you wearing last night, Sam?
SAM:	I wore these trainers.

(Sam places his foot alongside the print and presses it down. As he lifts it away, Jon peers over to inspect the footprint.)

JON:	Snap! Two footprints exactly the same. *(He grins.)* Looks like we've found our werewolf.
SAM:	That isn't funny. This is where I took the shortcut, remember.
ROBBO:	Hey, over here you two.
JON:	This is more like it … boot prints!
SAM:	See? Someone else has been here, too.
JON:	Someone wearing boots must have walked past this bush …
ROBBO:	… and turned into a wolf! The boot prints stop here and become animal prints.

JON:	*(Studies a piece of paper, which he has pulled from his pocket.)* They're wolf prints, all right. They match some tracks I downloaded from the computer.
SAM:	*(Shocked)* This is so unreal. You two are serious about this.
JON:	That wolf was after our blood.

(Suddenly they hear whistling. Jon, Robbo and Sam crouch down behind a bush as Mr Fowler enters. He is carrying wood which he throws onto the bonfire.)

ROBBO: He doesn't look happy.

SAM: He never does. *(Whispering.)* Look, he's wearing boots.

ROBBO: So?

SAM: If his boots match those prints, then the caretaker is …

JON: A weretaker!

ROBBO: Ha ha! Not necessarily. Fowler may have taken a shortcut through these bushes like you, Sam.

SAM: What are you saying? That there is no way of telling if he's a werewolf?

ROBBO: *(A pause)* We'd need to find his wolf skin.

SAM: Why don't you go and ask him?

(Mr Fowler adds more wood to his bonfire. It continues to glow gently.)

ROBBO: I'm not that stupid.

JON: So the question is, where would a werewolf
            keep its skin?

SAM: It could be anywhere. Buried out here. Locked
            in a cupboard …

JON: Stuffed under the floorboards …

ROBBO: No, if I were a werewolf I'd be more cunning
            than that. I would put my skin where everyone
            could see it.

JON: That's crazy!

ROBBO: Somewhere it would be seen every day.
            Somewhere no one would give it a second
            thought!

*(Robbo thinks deeply for a moment. Jon and Sam
look puzzled.)*

ROBBO: Wait here.

JON: Where are you going?

ROBBO: *(Grinning)* Just somewhere.

(Robbo runs off.)

SAM: What does he mean?

JON: I'm sure we'll find out!

SAM: You two seem to be getting on pretty well.

JON: Robbo's not so bad when you get to know
            him.

SAM:	You should hear yourself! He took your homework.
JON:	He gave it back.
SAM:	I don't trust him.
JON:	Maybe werewolves aren't the only ones who can change, Sam.

(Mr Fowler moves towards them, sniffing. He changes his mind and goes off. Robbo enters carrying a wolf skin under his arm.)

ROBBO:	I've got it.
JON:	Are you sure?
ROBBO:	Here. *(He tosses the wolf skin to Jon.)*

JON:	This is incredible. Hey, haven't I seen this before?
ROBBO:	Remember the time when we were kicked out of assembly for talking and had to see the headteacher?
JON:	You mean, because *you* were talking.
ROBBO:	I saw this inside her office.
SAM:	I've been in there and I didn't see a wolf skin.
ROBBO:	You mean you didn't notice it, Sam. Next to the headteacher's desk is a window, right?
JON:	No one can miss that.
ROBBO:	And on the floor there's a rug.
SAM:	If you say so.
ROBBO:	*(Speaking slowly)* A wolf … skin … rug.
JON:	Why didn't I think of that?

SAM:	*(Sneering)* Some people have been in that office more than others.
ROBBO:	You're no angel, yourself.
SAM:	So what do we do now, Sherlock?
ROBBO:	Catch us a werewolf. Fowler's definitely our man.
SAM:	You mean our 'wolf'.
JON:	How can you be so sure?
ROBBO:	*(Excited)* I've seen a sign! *(Sam and Jon look puzzled.)* On his office door … the one that says 'W.E.Fowler'.
SAM:	You call that proof?
ROBBO:	*(Smugly)* It's just another piece of the jigsaw slotting into place.

(Sam stares blankly at Robbo.)

ROBBO:	Rearrange the letters and what do you get?

(Sam shrugs. Robbo sighs and begins to spell it out.)

ROBBO:	W … E … R … E …
JON:	*(Finishing the spelling)* W … O … L … F!
SAM:	WEREWOLF. I wouldn't have spotted that in a million years.
ROBBO:	It's Fowler's idea of being clever. I bet Fowler, or whatever he's called, thinks we're just a bunch of dumb kids.

(Mr Fowler suddenly steps into view. Robbo grabs the wolf skin from Jon. Mr Fowler seems much taller and looks menacing. He sniffs the air, then stares wildly at Robbo.)

FOWLER: I think … that belongs to me.

ROBBO: This old thing?

(Robbo takes a step back from Mr Fowler.)

FOWLER: Let me see it.

ROBBO: It's just an old rug.

FOWLER: It's school property.

SAM: Then it doesn't belong to you.

FOWLER: Do you know who I am?

JON: We know *what* you are.

(Mr Fowler freezes for a moment, then smiles coldly.)

FOWLER: Really?

SAM: You're a wolf in caretaker's clothing.

FOWLER: You two had better go to your lessons before
            you get into trouble. *(To Robbo.)* You stay here.
            I want a word.

*(Sam looks at Robbo, who nods in the direction of the bonfire.
Sam grins, giving a sly thumbs-up sign.)*

ROBBO: Anything you say, Mr Fowler. *(Robbo backs
            away from Mr Fowler.)* Now, Sam!

*(Robbo throws the wolf skin to Sam who catches it and runs
towards the bushes.)*

FOWLER: *(Shouting)* I'll skin you alive!

*(Mr Fowler chases Sam, but is tackled by Jon. All three fall to
the ground. Sam throws the wolf skin towards Robbo.)*

SAM: Burn it, Robbo. Burn it!

(Mr Fowler gets to his feet and rushes towards the wolf skin.
Robbo reaches it first. He scoops it up, then holds it towards
the bonfire.)

ROBBO: Time to see what you're really made of!

(Robbo throws the wolf skin on the bonfire.)

FOWLER: You're too late! *(Falling to his knees.)*
              I have already left my mark.

SAM: You're finished!

FOWLER: I am free at last. *(To Jon and Robbo.)* But

            you can never rest. Beware the wolf!

(The weretaker howls and collapses in a heap.)

JON: What a way to go.

ROBBO: We did it!

SAM: *(Puzzled)* Beware the wolf. He said you had to

            beware the wolf.

JON: Not any more, Sam. The nightmare's over.

*(Jon, Robbo and Sam stand in silence for a moment, then
congratulate each other. Blackout.)*

Scene Five

That night, in Sam's bedroom. The room is lit by a full moon. Sam is talking in his sleep. In his dream, he remembers Mr Fowler standing in the shadows outside the old school building.

SAM: I must get home quickly ... I'll take a shortcut.

FOWLER: *(Quietly, from the shadows)* Beware.

SAM: Through the bushes ...

FOWLER: *(Menacingly)* Beware.

SAM: ... into the shadows.

FOWLER: *(Loudly)* Beware the night!

SAM: Something's there!

FOWLER: *(Triumphantly)* Beware the wolf!

SAM: No. *(Screaming.)* No!

(Sam sits up, suddenly awake. He is trembling. The room darkens as a cloud blocks the moonlight. Sam climbs out of bed and stumbles across to the window. He opens it in one movement.

Moonlight strikes Sam. For a second he freezes. Then slowly he stretches up, arches his back and howls.

One by one, the answering cries of other werewolves can be heard in the distance.)

SET A

It's Only an Animal
by Frances Usher

Runaway
by Jeremy Davies

SET B

Star Bores
by Steve Barlow and Steve Skidmore

Top of the Mops
by Julia Donaldson

SET C

The Big Time
by Jean Ure and Leonard Gregory

The Weekend War
by Tony Bradman

Sick as a Parrot
by Steve Barlow and Steve Skidmore

The Half Monty
by John Townsend

SET D

Honest
by Jon Blake

The Shadow
by Ritchie Perry

Arcade Games
by Jon Blake

Beware the Wolf
by Alan Dapré